SEASONS

SEASONS

A Poetry Collection by
Jean Kenward

Illustrated by Val Biro

BLACKIE

Copyright © 1989 Jean Kenward
Illustrations © 1989 Val Biro
This edition published 1989 by Blackie & Son Ltd

British Library Cataloguing in Publication Data

Kenward, Jean
Seasons.
I. Title
821'.914

ISBN 0-216-92756-0

Blackie and Son Ltd
7 Leicester Place
London WC2H 7BP

Typeset by Jamesway Graphics, Middleton, Manchester

Printed in Great Britain

Introduction

A poem is a moment of recognition breaking out into words. The first man who created the first poem must have been overwhelmed with wonder. Perhaps astonishment, and relief at the returning sun. Perhaps a sudden realization of powers beyond himself. Maybe just awareness of another dimension. Part of the turning world, he sang its praises.

A true poem still holds some element of mystery: that is its bloodstream. Children recognise this at a very early age; even before they understand the meaning of words, they are lulled or excited by the entrancing rhythms. These rhythms persist in the pattern of the natural environment which we all share, and nowhere more than in the steady flow of the seasons. A rule, an order, becomes apparent, but it is one of infinite variety, never the same. What child will not draw in its breath at the sight of the first snow falling? It may need a scientist to discover the design of each separate crystal, to tabulate and record it, but the poet in the child sees it, before he has words.

Sadly, modern life locks us away from so much. Few children walk to school any more, with time to loiter on the way home. Speed dominates. Darting into the continent and back on a package deal, how many miraculous details are drowned in distance? I talked to an artist, once, who declared he could spend the entire summer holiday looking at a field gate: considering what it was, what it might be, what it could suggest.

Seasons are sensuous, too: the smell, crunch and taste of them, frosted, smudged with mists, or swimming in a heat haze. Rain can be sniffed before a shower has started; snow fills the nostrils, pungent as a nut.

It is not necessary to live in the country to know these things. Migrating birds pass over cities and motorways on their hazardous journeys. Discarded railway tracks are vibrant with life. The parks thrive.

We all begin from different places of departure. But the pattern of the seasons is something to be shared; and, surely, we ourselves are a part of it.

Jean Kenward

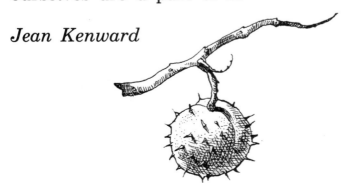

SPRING

A March Morning

A brightness came in with the morning
as gold as a Paradise bird.
There were ice pictures over the window
and a forest where nobody stirred.
There were fir trees and ferns, and a whiteness
that shone at the touch of the sun,
and melted . . . and faded . . . and vanished
as if it had never begun.

A lightness came in with the morning
that trembled and shook at a touch.
You could tell it was only just painted,
and everything, little or much,
was polished, and shone as if no one
had seen it, or known it, before.
A newness came in with the morning,
and winter went out of the door.

Cherry Blossom

I thought it was snow
    but the snow didn't come.
I thought it was rain
    but it wasn't.
I thought they were bees
    but they hadn't a hum . . .
Only petals kept falling
    and drifting

         and flowing
with some of them coming
    and some of them going
and none of them certain,
    and none of them knowing
the end of the journey—
    the quilt they were sewing
as white as new snow . . .
    but it wasn't.

Walls

I like a wall—
a wall to walk on,
a wall to jump off,
a wall to talk on.

It might be big
or it might be small,
as slim as a willow
or a boy-sized wall.

I like a wall
where snails are climbing
slower than slow,
their grey shells shining.

I like a wall
with bricks, and places
to put your toe in
and count your paces.

I like a wall
with flint and grit,
and a sun-warmed stone
in the heart of it.

Walls that are smooth
and walls with bumps on,
smothered with moss,
or sharp, with lumps on.

Walls that are narrow
and walls that are wider . . .
walls that are carrying
ant and spider.

Walls that are new
and pink and bold,
walls that are crumbling,
old . . . old . . .

And I know a wall
with a place to rest in
secret and snug—

it's got a nest in!

The Treasure

It is smooth and it is round,
set on tree or bush or ground—
and where it's hidden it is found.

It is blue, or white, or grey,
green, or anything you say,
speckled, splotched, or plain as day.

In its centre, walled alone,
naked as a pumice stone
grows a creature, flesh and bone.

When the time is ripe, it will
pierce the cover with its bill
and extend its tiny quill.

It is small and it is spry,
Sealed and darkened is its eye.
It has not learned how to fly.

What's the nature of its span?
Is it bird, or beast, or man?
Guess it, guess it if you can!

It is smooth and it is round.
Not a penny or a pound
serves to buy it, when it's found.

Spring Song

Have you ever seen
    such green, such green?
Have you ever seen
    such blue
as the woods in April
    when they blink
and a bit of the sky
    looks through?

And the light — the light
    is tiny and bright
in every blob
    of dew?

Have you ever seen
    such green, such green?
Have you ever seen
    such blue?

Rooks nesting

'Caw!' says the Rook.
  He rises
    and flaps a bit.
Up comes the wind,
  and carries
    him off with it . . .

'Caw!' cries the Rook.
  He settles
    down on his nest.
'Caw! I have brought
  another
    twig to the rest!'

'Caw!' says his wife.
  'You aren't
    the only one—
I have been busy too.
  The nest's
    half-done.'

'Caw!' they both cry.
   Just look
      up here! You'll see
a dozen windy nests
      in each
         tall tree!'

Butterfly

Butterfly on the wall—
    butterfly, with your blue
and decorated wings—
    How do you do?

April is in the air,
    the frost is gone.
What was it made you put
    your colours on?

All winter long your wings
    were folded close
in a dark, secret place . . .
    Nobody knows

How the sun touched you with
    his finger, then
told you the spring had come.
    O when, O when

You felt his burning gold
    what did you do?
Did you fly after him—
    blue into blue?

17

SUMMER

Cow Parsley

Cow Parsley up to my shoulder,
cow parsley up to my nose . . .
It's full of the scent of the summer—
wherever I'm walking, it blows.

I sneeze and I snuffle and sniff it.
I shake all the bits off my shirt;
there are millions of miniature flowers
like pepper dust over my skirt.

Cow parsley up to my shoulder,
towering out of the grass,
so tall that I'm tangled between it
and no one can see where I pass.

But the bees keep on busily buzzing,
no matter what petals may fall.
Do they wonder whatever I'm doing
caught here, in the heart of it all?

Wind

I had the wind at my back.
I had the wind on my face—
I ran with the wind.
      I said
Wind, let us run a race!

I had the wind in my hair,
I had the wind in my hand.
Faster than rain
      we ran
till we reached the edge of the land:

The green sea rushed and shone,
the wind flew over the sea,
and I called
      I called to the wind,
and the wind called back to me.

Then a sudden stillness came:
the wind had twisted and gone.
I turned, and I wandered home . . .
      but the wind
            went on.

Swallows

Tell me how
    the swallows go,
quick and nimble,
    to and fro?

        When the sun
            is in the sky,
        up and up
            the swallows fly
        chasing all
            the winds that blow,
        to and fro,
            to and fro . . .

But when there's
   a scent of rain—
down and down
   they dip again
till their breasts
   are on the grass,
almost touching
   as they pass.

     While the months
        of summer flow,
     sometimes high
        and sometimes low
     up and down,
        and to and fro . . .
     That is how
        the swallows go.

Four folk

Who can fly?
Who can fly?
'I,' said the eagle,
'in the sky,
over the mountain
heaven – high.
Watch me, won't you?
I can fly!'

'Look at me,
look at me,'
(whispered the small fish
in the sea),
and he boasted
he could swim
with all the ocean
under him.

'Earth is round,
earth is round,'
murmured the earthworm
in the ground.
'Soft and slow,
soft and slow—
that's the safest
way to go.'

'Thump and shout!
Thump and shout!'
called the schoolboy
running out.
Before he'd finished
what he'd said
he turned his heels
over his head!

Thrush

Fat fellow with
   a speckled coat—
who put such music
   in your throat?

Who wound you up
   and let you sing
as loud as any
clockwork thing?

You never seem
   to tire, or say
'It is too wet
   for me today.'

And I have known
   black thunder fill
the sky, and leave you
   singing still!

Badgers

There are badgers here in the woods.
Their gaping tunnels
have a mystery about them—
a sense of dark.
If you look in the leaves
you'll discover a secret footprint . . .
Hid from the bright sky
and the lifting lark
the badgers blunder and pad
with a burly, solid
purpose,
seeking their small and delicate prey;
nuzzling for roots,
streaked with a white flamboyance
over their forehead—
broad in its grizzled grey.

Sea Horse

I saw on the sea
a white horse with no rider,
O wildly and joyfully
tossing his mane!

He sprang from a stable
beyond the Atlantic
without any road to it,
paddock or lane.

He came from the sunset
so fiery and splendid,
and long after darkness
had fallen and spread

I saw in the moonlight
a horse with no rider,
but sequins and silver
about him instead.

At Night

Some people are afraid of the dark.
I like it.
I like its softness and its mystery;
and dark is gentle to the touch.
It gathers
into its sweetness
moth and bird and tree.

If you should think unhappy things,
remember
the white, bright, needle-pointed early star
friendly to strangers,
comforting and splendid,
blessing the rain-wet roof tops
where we are.

29

Spider

There's a creature up there—
I can see it—
a little, peculiar
thing . . .
It hasn't got horns,
tail, or prickles,
it hasn't got even
a wing.
It hangs upside down
on the ceiling,
in the crack which is close
to the door,
and it's busy—
it's terribly busy—
with its feet, yet it hasn't
a paw.

It hasn't got fingers
or ankles
but it runs—it's as fast
as a ball;
it has several eyes,
yet I'm certain
it doesn't wear glasses
at all;

it sews and it weaves
and it crochets
without any needle
or pin,
and it stretches a web
out of nothing . . .
But how does a spider
begin?

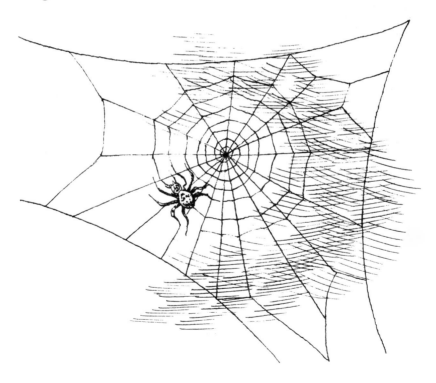

Woodlice

Deep in a crumbling
darkness, crisply armoured
against attack,
grey woodlice are assembled,
dry and silent,
cushioned in cleft and crack.

Cold, spherical,
steel-hard, they fold their tiny
bodies so tight
as to allow
no entry to the summer's
pervasive light;

Only—at a brief
raising of the curtain—
in sudden, wild hysteria, they run
this way and that,
unrolling, unprotected,
unloosed, undone,

Certain that without
any word or warning,
each one must brace
himself to bear
the bird-infested morning,
and the sun's face.

Ladybirds

Ladybird
 with seven spots
running through
 forget-me-nots
with your bright
 and lacquered wing—
like a jewel
 in a ring.

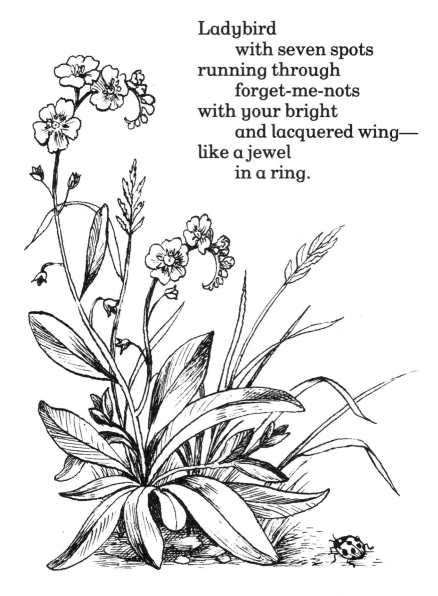

What a world
    you travel there!
Grasses fine
    as ladies' hair
seem as thick
    as rope to you,
as you push
    a passage through.

When my shadow
    touches stone,
do you guess
    that day has gone?
And wonder
    when I move a bit
how sudden brightness
    lightens it?

Does a snail
    seem to be
as fierce as tigers are
    to me?
Ladybird
    with painted skin—
what a world
    you travel in!

AUTUMN

Autumn Song

Have you seen
  the lamps of autumn?
Have you seen them
  glow
through the woodland's
  tattered branches
when the winds
  blow?

Have you touched
  the leaves of autumn—
yellow, red
  and brown,
caught and held them
  for a moment
as they travelled
  down?

Have you found
　　the mists of autumn?
Have you watched them
　　wear
shafts of gold
　　and rings of silver?
Tell me,
　　where?

A Wind is Blowing

A wind is blowing
  the conkers down
Biff! Bang! Bump!
  Inside every shell's
a brown
        chestnut lump—
Put your heel
  upon the spine
(Gently, gently!
  That one's mine!)
Polish them
  and see them shine.
Thwick thwack thump!

The wind is blowing
    the nuts about
Slip! Slap! Slop!
    Crack the shells
and get them out
    when they drop.
Try them with
    your teeth, and see
if they're ripe
    as they should be.
Some for you
    and some for me.
Tip tap top!

The Road

I like this road:
it's full of bumps
and lumps and puddles,
stones and flints.
The sides are marked
with broken stumps
and hedges where
new treasure glints;
a sparrow's nest
with eggs I found,
and hazelnuts,
and once—a string
of berries, and
a mistle thrush
who tried to teach me
how to sing.

I like this road:
it's rough and plain
and good for walking folk
who see
the small and strange
and secret things . . .
At least, it's good enough
for me.

Seeds in a packet

Seeds in a packet
small and dry,
can you hear
when the wind goes by?

Can you tell
when the sun is out,
and bees and butterflies
roam about?

Do you fidget
when the rain
falls so quietly
in our lane?

Seeds in a packet
not yet sown,
will you remember
when you're grown?

What it felt like
when you were
little as dust
and light as air?

Snail

How wet it is! How wet!
The rain is falling
faster than words can say
or drenched birds, calling.

The snail—he likes it, though!
He leaves a long
slithery, silvered track . . .
Giving no song.

Only the silence of
his secret shell
shows that he can go out,
and in as well.

Tender and small he is:
a gentle thing,
sipping with soft, grey lip,
and wandering . . .

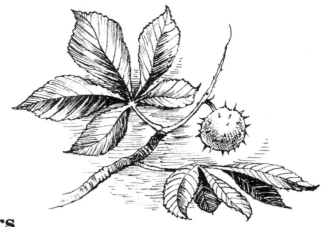

Conkers

Can you see
 what I can see—
a conker hanging
 in the chestnut tree?

Can you see
 his spiky shell?
Can you see him smile,
 as well?

That's a sign
 he's ready now
to fall—to tumble
 from the bough . . .

Here he comes
 with thump and plop—
Watch him!
 Watch the chestnuts drop!

Windfalls

Apple tree,
apple tree,
drop an apple
down to me—
green or scarlet
let it be,
windy, bendy
apple tree!

Other creatures
cross or kind
have pricked and pocked
the apple rind—
some have even tunnelled in
and found a feast
beneath the skin!

So let the flesh show
creamy white—
sweet or sour—
when I bite,
and inside it
let me see
pips to make
another tree . . .

46

The Kite

Up on the top
of Birdlip Hill
I saw a person
standing still;
I saw a person
with a string,
and at the end of it
a thing
that dived and soared
and leaped and fell . . .
and rose again . . .
I could not tell
whether it were
a bird in flight—
it was so airy
and so light—
and yet he held it
on a string.
It tugged and tugged
like anything,
and still he would not
let it go
but hung onto
the coil below,
and up it climbed
and down, and then

in lilting spirals
up again.
He laughed to watch it
plunge and play.

I nearly saw him
blow away.

Owl

The owl knows it's autumn:
'To – whit, to – whoo!' he cries,
and heavily he lumbers forth
and out of darkness flies.

He knows the frost, he knows the frail
cobweb on leaf and tree,
but best of all he knows the stars
in their great galaxy;

And among all those countless eyes,
steady and round and trim,
shadowed with different rocks and seas
the moon looks down on him.

Deer

There are deer in the woods.
They are shy and mysterious.
They're afraid to be seen,
or to come too close to us.
But sometimes, on misty days
you may glimpse one roving
from shade to shade . . .
or discover a stillness, moving . . .

The woods are theirs.
They dwell in a secret world
of bracken and bark,
intent on their own affairs,
not wanting to mix
with the curious ways of men.
Like snow, they come . . .
   Like snow they are gone again . . .

WINTER

The Camel's Carol

The long walk,
  the heat,
    the great burdens,
and sand
  always sand
    under our feet;
and sometimes
  a pool,
    a day's pasture,
and cool
  water—cool,
    yes, and sweet,

Until,
  with our silks
    and our spices
we came
  to the stable,
    and met
the Child
  taking milk

from His mother.
And so
   He received us.
     And yet

I had known kings.
   I had laboured
for princes,
   but never
     before
bowed
   to a child
     in a manger.
Great
   was the glory
     we saw!

Come, bird, come.

Come, bird, come—
the nut's on the string,
the fat's in the basket
as fine as anything,
the crumb's on the table
the crust's on the floor—
take a little, break a little . . .
now a little more!

Come, bird, come—
the frost's on the spray,
the berries are crusted
with ice this winter day;
the moon has forgotten
to put herself to bed.
Take a little, break a little
good brown bread!

Winter came . . .

Winter came suddenly.
A single spray
carried a bloom of frost
as white as may.

Someone had painted with
enchanted breath
ferns on the window pane,
and flower, and leaf.

Snow fell in delicate
spirals, and then
waited a moment, and
was gone again.

Winter came suddenly,
without a word
warning us. If there was—
nobody heard.

The Traveller

Early today
    I put my shoe
in a new place—
    the other, too!
I stepped where none
    had been before,
twelve paces
    from my kitchen door.
And yet, I take
    this common way
on every morning—
    every day . . .

No other mark
   there was, except
my own, new printed
   since I slept;
I seemed to be
   a traveller, sent
into a quilted
   continent,
where all was strange
   and smooth, and white . . .
Fresh snow had fallen
   overnight.

Windy Hill

Come with me!
    Where are you going?
Up the great hill
 where the wind always wanders,
and won't keep still.

Even on winter days,
 when the snow's whiteness
covers the meadows with
 a new-born brightness,
a wind is found up there,
 high up, and calling
in his old, lonely voice,

rising . . . and falling . . .

Even on summer days
    when the earth's sleeping
in a long stillness—sure
    a wind is leaping
on the high hilltop.

Come . . .
        it's where we'll find him
now, with all sky above,
    and earth behind him!

Fox

There's somebody on the path
ahead of us.
We can follow his footprints
over the fallen snow—
a scatter of dark shapes,
silent and secretive.
It could be a fox.
This way, the foxes go
into the woodland.
Yes, it might well be so.

And there he stands by the larches,
bold and still,
the colour of apricots,
his splendid brush
close to the ground!
A long, slow look at us,
and he turns
to move serenely off.
Although
we could have shouted,
we stayed, to watch him go
through his own dominion,
proud, and mysterious,
quietly padding over the late, soft snow . . .

Footprints

Have you seen the path to the woods?
It is marked with small
circles and blobs
in a scatter of fresh snowfall.

Creatures have gathered here—
though you'd hardly guess
so many would venture
out of their secretness.

How bright it is on the path!
The shining air
quivers, as if a watchful eye
were there . . .

Hidden by leaf or twig
there's a fieldmouse. Food,
(or the wish for food)
brings everyone out of the wood.

The timid, who left these marks
in dell and ditch
must have been hungry
so to tremble and twitch,

Leaving their footprints
over the newest snow.
They are quickly covered . . . soon
nothing will show.

Icicle Joe

I made a snowman:
Icicle Joe.
The moon shone round him
high and low . . .
The moon shone round him
sides and back—
it gave him a shadow,
purple-black.

I made a snowman
white and plump;
a nose he had
like a sugar lump.
The sun shone round him . . .
One bright day
he slumped a little
and went away,

Vanishing softly
bit by bit
like a lollipop does
when you suck at it.
Only a puddle
stayed to show
where I had built him—
Icicle Joe.

Waking

Deep in the ground,
under the snow,
small and secretive
creatures go:
worms, with damp
and satin skin,
wriggle and tunnel
further in . . .
Snails, with patterns
on their shell
probe a passage
there, as well.
Things so tiny,
things so small
you hardly see
their shape at all,
stay alive
and hide themselves
where the beetle
digs and delves.

Under the frost,
after the snow,
seeds of summer
sleep. They know
a time will come
when each will thrust
up and up
and—fit to bust—
break into
a flush of light.
Sure, it won't be
always night!
Sure, they'll feel
an April shower
when it is
their waking hour?
Sure, the sweet
and shining air
will reach and touch them,
even there?
Deep in the ground,
little and low,
who can tell us
what they know?

Walking on Ice

Walking on ice
is rather nice,
your feet go click
and clack!
But if it splits
in splintered bits
you tumble
on your back!

Walking in snow
is soft, and so
you scarcely ever
fall;
but if you do—
why shouldn't you?
It hardly hurts
at all!

Jack Frost

Jack Frost has been again
this winter night:
the lawn is white as flour,
and the roofs white.

I touched a puddle with
my winter shoe;
the frozen water creaked,
and crackled, too.

Squeak! went the ice. Ice hung
upon the fence:
silver it was, like fifty
silver pence.

Jack Frost has been again
this winter day—
left a great whiteness here,
and gone away.

The Traveller

Come down and tell me
what you know,
Arctic swallow
from the Arctic snow!

How many miles
have you flown
since your feather
first was grown?

How many countries
have you crossed,
by wind and wave
and tempest tossed?

Swerving, swinging
faster yet—
do you remember
or forget

Hunger, thirst
and heat and snow?
Come down and tell me
what you know!

Christmas Morning

Today I woke up in the dark
in Christmas joy.
The moon still hung in the sky,
like a Christmas toy.

I felt at the foot of my bed.
Something was there,
darker than darkness. Heavy
it was, and square.

And from the top of my sock
bulged—who knows what?
I thought: shall I open it now,
right now, or not?

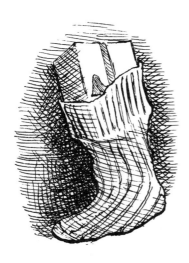

I waited. Silent it was.
Nobody stirred.
Perhaps it was midnight still?
And then, a bird

Called out of the cold air
where it was hid—
Open it! Open it now!
And so I did.

Index of First Lines